Usborne
Little Wipe-Clean
Dot-to-Dot

Illustrated by Malu Lenzi

Designed by Jenny Addison

Written by Kirsteen Robson

1 2 3 4 5 6 7 8 9 10

Connect the sets of dots in number order, to see what else is swimming in the sea.

Make patterns on the turtles' shells.

1 2 3 4 5 6 7 8 9 10

Connect the sets of dots in number order, to finish the creepy crawlies.

4

3   5

2   6

1   7

Finish the caterpillar by
drawing over the dotted lines.

Give the
bee some
stripes.

1   2

3

6

5   4

1 2 3 4 5 6 7 8 9 10

Connect the sets of dots in number order, to finish the spaceships, astronaut and star.

Make a pattern
on the planet.

1 2 3 4 5 6 7 8 9 10

Connect the sets of dots in number order, to finish the picture.

Find and circle 4 rabbits.

Draw over the dotted
line to finish the bird.

Draw more food in
the bird feeder.

1 2 3 4 5 6 7 8 9 10

Connect the sets of dots in number order, to finish the boats.

Make patterns on the sails.

Find and circle 5 gulls.

1 2 3 4 5 6 7 8 9 10

Connect the sets of dots in number order, to finish the prehistoric animals.

Draw over the dotted lines to finish the plates on the ankylosaur's back and the club on its tail.

Draw over the dotted lines
to finish the volcano smoke.

Find and circle 4
dinosaur nests.

1 2 3 4 5 6 7 8 9 10

Connect the sets of dots in number order, to finish 3 robots.

Draw over the dotted lines to finish this robot.

6 1
5
4 3
6 ———— 1
5 2
4 3

Find and circle 3 robo-mice.

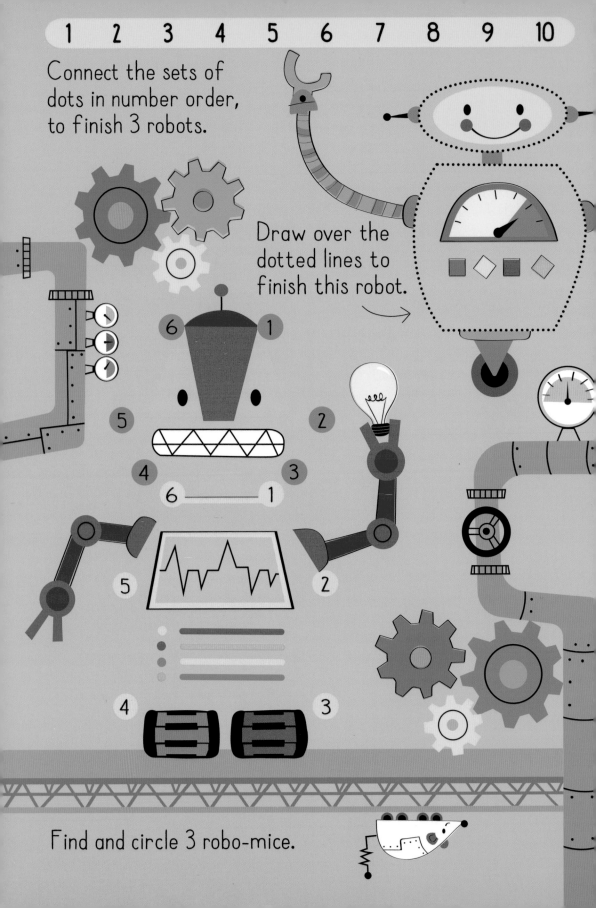

Give this
robot a face.

1 2 3 4 5 6 7 8 9 10

Connect the sets of dots in number order, to see what else lives in or near the pond.

Draw over the dotted lines
to finish the lily pads.

Find and circle
6 dragonflies.

1 2 3 4 5 6 7 8 9 10

Connect the sets of dots in number order, to finish the truck, tractor and car.

Draw 2 wheels on this car.

Find and circle
3 dogs.

1 2 3 4 5 6 7 8 9 10

Connect the sets of dots in number order, to finish the monsters.

Find and circle 5 yellow monster flies.